ooh la la!

perfect makeup

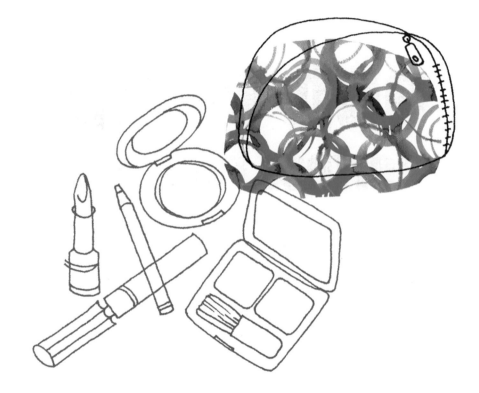

ooh la la!
perfect makeup

Susie Galvez

Illustrated by Chico Hayasaki

MQP

Published by MQ Publications Limited
12 The Ivories
6–8 Northampton Street
London, N1 2HY
email: mail@mqpublications.com
website: www.mqpublications.com

Illustrator: Chico Hayasaki/www.cwc-i.com
Editor: Laura Kesner
Senior Designer: Victoria Bevan

ISBN: 1-84072-592-3
10 9 8 7 6 5 4 3 2 1

Printed and bound in France by *Partenaires-Livres*® (JL)

Contents

Introduction

Who says making up is hard to do? All you need is a little color and a little paint to make you look like what you ain't!

But before you pick up the liquid eyeliner and start wielding the mascara wand with the wild abandon of a '70s glam rock band, take down some superstar how-to tips from *Ooh La La! Perfect Makeup*.

Learn how to let your lips make a statement without saying a word. Express your inner star with cha-ching cheek color and add pow to your brow with tweeze tips. Brush up on what tools are a must-have in your beauty kit and which ones you should toss right now. Face up to new eye shadow colors and find out what shade is most flattering for your skin tone.

From luscious lips and sparkling smiles, to melt-proof mascara and powder with staying power, *Ooh La La! Perfect Makeup* knows all the tricks.

Let the show begin!

Chapter 1

In the details

Pretty is as pretty does

Even though some beauty items do not have to be expensive to produce excellent results, sometimes you just need an indulgence or two. Maybe the plain powder compact is a little cheaper, but the one with rhinestones catches your eye and makes you feel pretty. Buy the pretty one. You will love it each and every time you use it, so the cost is well worth the indulgence. Have a couple of extra-special items in your beauty bag to enjoy what being an "Ooh La La" lady is all about.

Bag lady

Carry all your makeup items in a makeup bag. It keeps your products together in one place, cleanly and neatly. Retouching your powder and lip color is a snap because you know exactly where to find it. Plus, changing handbags is a breeze—just grab the makeup bag and go.

Lifting the veil

The current trend in makeup colors is transparency. Because of new technology, colors that previously looked harsh or garish are now more subtle and more flattering to the face. In most color products you will find hints of copper, gold, bronze, mauve, or lavender. Because of this blending, almost anyone can wear any color. The trick is to blend well and to pick a harmonious palette. A brown is no longer a brown; it is now sometimes the color of mink or milk chocolate with a bit of glimmer added. Blush has soft varieties of color instead of one flat color. Take time to experiment and create fun, new looks. Remember, making up is like building a sand castle, it washes away every night!

Splurge savvy

When creating the perfect makeup collection, knowing what products are worth spending extra money on and what products can be bought at a bargain is worth its weight in gold. For best results, opt to spend a little more on skin care products. It takes more money to include active ingredients, so you can truly see and feel the difference.

Other items not to skimp on are foundation, face powder, and blush. High-end foundation, powder, and blush offer more finely produced pigments to help color match the skin, so you actually use less product. High-end powders are also pressed more compactly, allowing more applications than cheaper brands.

Get plenty of bang for your buck with bargain lip pencils, eye pencils, eye shadows, mascaras, and even lipstick. You will only have to look in your makeup bag to see virtually every color of the rainbow. Purchasing these items at bargain prices will allow you to justify the quantity!

Prime the canvas

Before a painter begins a masterpiece, the canvas is always primed. Priming seals the canvas, preserves the paint, and allows for flawless brush strokes. To correctly prime your "facial canvas," apply moisturizer, and allow to absorb into the skin for ten minutes before beginning any makeup application. Moisturizer not only protects the skin from the elements, but also plumps up the skin and allows for smooth application of foundation. Could you imagine looking great with taut, dry skin? Prime your canvas.

I wonder

When trying to decide if a product needs
to be tossed, here are some guidelines.
If it looks or smells funny, toss it.
Keep all products out of direct
sunlight. If you are taking
sunscreen to the beach with
you, stash it in a dark place,
such as under a blanket or in
your beach bag. If any product has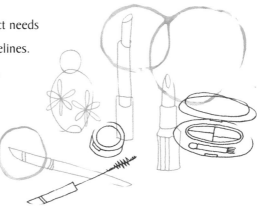
separated, shake it; if it still looks like oil and vinegar dressing, toss it.
Never, ever, add saliva to a product that has dried out—throw it away.
Keep containers closed; air is the enemy for product preserving. A tried
and true rule: when in doubt, throw it out!

Clean scene

It is not a good idea to use cosmetic counter testers on the face. With the amount of store traffic, it is very difficult, if not impossible, to keep the testers bacteria-free. Opt instead to test a product on the back of the hand or on your fingertips. Use a fresh cotton ball or cotton swab to wipe the area clean and then test with another applicator.

Less is more

If you are using extra amounts of cosmetics to look younger, you are missing the message. As you age, you actually need less coverage in order to achieve an "ageless look." In the professional modeling world, the rule is, the younger the model, the more makeup you use—in order to make the model look older. Think about this when applying your own makeup. Cosmetics used in excess can accentuate your age.

She is out for the evening

If work time turns into evening-out time, and you don't have time to completely redo your makeup, this two-minute tip will take you from professional to glamorous in a snap.

Moisten a couple of cotton balls with skin toner. Lightly cleanse chin, nose, and forehead. Using a sponge, add fresh foundation to areas just cleansed. Dust with powder. Add blush and lightly powder again. Add a sexy color of eye shadow, such as gold or bronze, line eyes with a smoky liner, and add another coat of mascara. Put a deeper lip color on and add a dash of frosted lip gloss to the center of the lips—press lips together and go!

A-B-C

Schedule a professional makeup lesson—not a session. A makeup lesson is
where the professional teaches you how to do your makeup for both day and
evening. A session is where you have makeup applied. A session is good for
one day—a lesson is good for a lifetime. The makeup artist will show you
how to bring out your best features. In most cases, the makeup artist will do
one half of your face to show you how, and where to apply the products, and
you will try to copy their application on the other side of your face. That way,
the next morning in your dressing area, with no one else around, you will
be able to do it yourself—professionally.

To the point

Keep eye, lip, and brow pencils sharp. A dull point will cause an imperfect
application every time. It does not take much, just a quick turn or two on
the sharpener. Don't over-sharpen, as you will waste the product. Plus,
sharpening the point removes any nasty bacteria picked up on previous
contact with the skin.

Zoom lens

After having a professional brow makeover, take a close-up shot of your brows. You will have a snapshot of how your brows should look. Keep the photo handy to help direct tweezing in between scheduled brow appointments. Snapshots of makeup sessions are also great in order to help you recreate the look.

Brow zing!

One of the most common and noticeable eyebrow mistakes is brows that look drawn on. People should not see your eyebrows coming before they see you.

To get eyebrows headed in the right direction, brush brows downward and then across and back into position with a small brow brush or a toothbrush dedicated for this task. Apply brow color and blend, blend, blend.

Exercise your options

Decide here and now to exercise without makeup on.
Firstly—who are you trying to impress?
Secondly—you will probably never see these people again. And if you do see them, you don't want to be remembered with smears, drips, and splotches! Work out with a clean face, sporting only a dab of moisturizer if necessary. Wipe the sweat off your face with a towel, and drink plenty of water as you exercise. The skin will reward you with a rosy glow and luminous appearance.

The big sweep

When dusting excess powder away from the skin, use your powder brush in light downward strokes to help prevent the powder from getting caught in the fine hairs on the sides of the face and jawline. Pay particular attention to these areas, as powder will collect most readily here, making the hairs more noticeable. Trust me, the hairs are there!

Beauty marks the spot

Suddenly a blemish appears but you have no time to treat it. Why not morph the blemish into a beauty mark?

Begin by calming the blemish down. Dab it with a cotton ball soaked in a gentle astringent. After the area has dried, draw your beauty mark dot over the top with an eyebrow pencil. (This is better than using an eyeliner pencil, since it has a drier texture and is less likely to smudge.)

Finally, set your beauty mark in place with a light dusting of loose powder. Make your mark!

20/20

Sometimes eyeglasses distort your eyes and your eye makeup. Near-sighted lens have a tendency to make eyes appear smaller. To counteract this reduction, opt for brighter, bolder shadows and lots of mascara to ensure that your eyes do not disappear.

If you are far-sighted, your lens could make your eyes look bigger and your eye makeup more prominent. Better to opt for more muted colors that won't seem so obvious.

Check out the new eyeglass styles. With new technology, the glass almost seems to disappear, allowing the eyes to shine through. Ask your optician.

There she blows

Always dry your hair before applying your makeup. You can wait to style your hair after you apply your makeup if you would like, but dry it first. The heat from the dryer can make you perspire and cause your makeup to smudge—you want your makeup to be long-lasting and fresh, so wait to do it last.

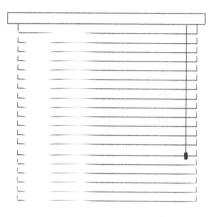

Another point of view

Sometime, just for fun, get together with a girlfriend and do each other's makeup. You will be amazed at how people picture you, even if you have been lifelong friends. Plus, it is a great way to find a new look!

Into the looking glass

No makeup area is complete without a magnifying mirror. A magnifying mirror allows you see up close and to catch any smears, unblended areas, or other makeup mistakes that you might not see in a regular mirror. Plus, it is great for tweezing the brows precisely and for capturing the occasional chin hairs that crop up overnight!

Purchase a travel-size magnifying mirror as well. Although some hotels have them, it is always best to have one handy.

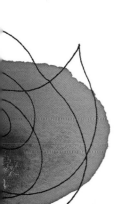

Chapter 2

Let's face it

Foundation of foundation

When it comes to finding the perfect foundation, the trick is texture. The texture of the foundation needs to work in harmony with the texture of your skin. Sometimes skin needs a little more coverage than at other times. Plus, as we age, our skin loses its luminosity. We can return a bit of radiance to the skin with a foundation formula that lends life and adds a soft glow. As a rule, liquid is better than cream foundation. Cream has a tendency to be heavy and thick looking on the surface. Powder foundations are great if a matte finish is desired, but be careful not to pick an overly drying one.

Seasons of the year can also affect the way a foundation looks and feels. Warmer weather calls for lighter formulas that are sheer like our warm weather clothes. Maybe a tinted moisturizer is all you really need for those all-too-hot days.

Keep it sheer

Did you know that 90 percent of foundation products on the cosmetic market are too pink-based? Why, since most of us need more yellow-based products to avoid looking overly pink or red? A good foundation contains a fair amount of beige pigment, which is yellow-based in order to create a natural blank canvas on the skin. We add color via eye shadows, blushes, and lip colors. If our foundation adds color, the tendency is to look clown-like—certainly not the effect we are aiming for. Opt for a neutral yellow-based foundation for the best results.

Dots right

To apply perfect foundation every time, use the dot method. Put foundation on a wedged sponge. Dot on forehead, cheeks, chin, and tip of nose. Connect the dots by gently blending in upward and outward motions. Blend toward the hairline and glide down toward the jawbone. After getting foundation in place, take the sponge and lightly smooth down on the cheek toward the jaw to help any facial hairs lie down properly.

Tone up

Instead of water to moisten foundation, spritz a little oil-free toner on the sponge to moisten before applying color. You will get the slip that you need to spread the foundation, as well as a little skin care treat. Oil-free toner can also be used to re-moisten a slightly dry, water-based formula.

Undercover

The right concealer is a gift you should give yourself. It can cover dark circles, blemishes, sunspots, and create a perfect face. Before applying foundation, put a small amount onto the ring finger and gently pat underneath the eye area until the product warms up enough to spread. Pat on any other areas that are red, blemished, or just need better coverage. Apply enough product so that when add your foundation and move it around with your sponge, you will not remove all of the concealer, but rather allow the concealed areas to go undetected.

Powder power

Powder does for makeup what hair spray does for hair. It sets the makeup, allowing it to last. Powder can be pressed or loose. The formula should be finely milled, soft to the touch, and easy to apply. The finer the powder is, the more flawless the finish. Loose powder is excellent for setting makeup upon application, while pressed is best to carry with you while you are on the go. In either case, powder is a must-have for any makeup application to be complete.

To apply loose powder, swirl the powder brush into the powder. Tap brush to remove excess and apply to face in big sweeping motions, starting at the forehead and continuing down the face. Should any extra powder remain on the face, redust with the powder brush or remove with a makeup sponge.

If you want to keep touch-ups to a minimum, put a bit of extra powder on the brush and gently pat onto facial areas with a slight tapping motion to really set the product. Great for shine-prone areas such as nose, forehead, and chin.

Cake date

If you notice any of your powdered makeup items beginning to look and feel cakey, it is because they are coated with your skin's oils. Take a flat edge, such as a butter knife, and gently scrape off the caked surface on top. The product underneath is once again fresh and new.

Oil embargo

If excessive oil due to hormonal fluxes is causing your foundation to turn orange, try this. Mix a spoonful of bicarbonate of soda into your loose face powder, and then lightly dust the powder mixture over your skin before applying your foundation. The bicarbonate of soda will give your skin a slightly acid pH level to prevent the foundation from turning orange. This is a great tip for overly-humid, summer days too!

Under wraps

Keep the cellophane or paper on the top of translucent powder containers. Instead of removing the entire cover and risking spillages or waste, prick a few holes in the top and shake the powder out into the container's top or your hand for easier application. To use, simply put your big powder brush into the container's lid to collect the powder you have shaken out, or rub your brush in your hand to load the brush for powder application. You will find that your application amount will be just enough and that none is wasted.

Keep smiling

For best blush results, apply a light dusting of face powder to the areas on which you are going to add blush. By adding a bit of powder to the face before adding blush, you will keep the blush from mixing with foundation and possibly changing color. It also lessens the likelihood of streaks or blush fade-out. Powdering afterward with a light dusting of face powder over where you have applied your blush will set the blush color for the very longest lasting application.

Into the dark

Contouring is a technique that uses darker powders, blushes, or bronzers to give the face the illusion of a more defined bone structure. Once limited to a professional makeup artist's hand, now anyone can do it with the proper technique and tools. Use a contour brush. A contour brush is closer cropped than a powder brush, as well as tighter in structure to allow you to apply a small amount of product evenly.

To contour the cheeks, suck them in slightly, and stroke the contour toward the top of where the hollow begins—then move the brush upward, toward the ear where the hollow ends.

To thin down a thicker nose, glide the contour on each side of the nose. To lessen a double chin, blend the contour downward under the jawline—this time using your large powder brush to get a softer effect.

In all cases, contouring should be done before applying powder. Face powder will help to soften the look as well as set the contour.

Into the light

Highlighting is adding light to an area you want to bring forward or emphasize. Most of the time, highlighters have a touch of shimmer or glitter added to them. Highlighters can be shimmery powders, creams in jars or in stick-form. Choose any method you like. Bring out your cheeks by applying highlighter over the apples of them. Highlight the eyes by applying highlighter at the arch just under each brow. Also apply the shimmer both at the beginning and the tail of the brow. Remember, if you opt for cream highlighter, it goes on after you apply your facial powder to keep it from streaking.

Bronze goddess

Bronzer is a wonderful way to add a sun-kissed look to the face without the sun damage. The key word is "sun-kissed"—not suntan. Use lightly on the places that the sun would touch, such as the cheeks, the nose, the forehead, and the chin. Do not attempt to use a bronzer all over the face as the effect will look dirty, hardly the effect you want. Also remember, less is more. Until you know how the product applies, start with a tiny bit and then add more. Adding more to the face is much easier than having to take it off, if applied too heavily.

Order in the house

Whether you are a blush-and-go gal, or one who enjoys a full range of makeup products, a product application order is critical to the success of your overall finished look.

Begin with perfection products such as (1) eye shadow primer; (2) concealer; (3) lip color stabilizer. Then move on to the facial products such as (4) foundation; (5) cream blush; (6) face powder; (7) powder blush; (8) face powder over blushed areas. Next go for the eyes with (9) base color of eye shadow; (10) eyeliner; (11) eye shadow contour color; (12) brow color; and (13) mascara. Finally it is time for (14) lip liner; and (15) lip color.

You may not use all of the steps, but when completed in this order, makeup stays on longer, looks more believable, and application time is cut down to only 15 minutes maximum!

Peek-a-boo

Freckles are the result of too much sun exposure. To keep yours to a minimum, always wear sunscreen. Don't attempt to completely cover your facial freckles with concealer or foundation, since all you will end up with is a thick mask-like appearance. Freckles are charming and can look very pretty. Enjoy yours—but remember to protect your skin.

Smoke and mirrors

Buying the perfect foundation doesn't have to be a magic act. To make it happen, all you need is a good source of natural light and a mirror in which to check the color and coverage on your skin. Fluorescent and halogen lights are totally misleading and cast shadows and discolorations on the skin—natural light is definitely best.

The back of the hands are not good color matches at all. Just compare the back of your hand to your face—altogether different. The inner part of the wrist is helpful in gauging coverage. Apply a small amount on the veins on the inside of the wrist to see how well it covers.

The best place to test foundation is a clean jawline. The perfect foundation color for you will blend with your skin instantly, like magic!

I am blushing

Blush is an amazing product. It adds a bit of bloom to the face to give a fresh healthy glow. It creates a slight contour, allowing the face to look more angled, if so desired. And my favorite feature—blush can create an instant facelift. As we all know, gravity constantly pulls the skin down. But adding a bit of blush on the cheeks instantly gives lift and creates a fresh, youthful look!

To apply, start at the ear level and gently sweep the blush brush back and forth toward the middle of the cheeks and upward toward the temples. This technique creates a comma-type effect around the eye and on the cheek. After completing eye makeup and lip color, check to see if a bit more blush is needed to balance the face. But do wait until the rest of the face is completed before adding more blush since you may tend to compensate by adding more eye shadow and lip color to match the cheeks.

Cream dream

Sometimes powder blush appears to be cakey or may settle on dry skin emphasizing dry areas. To avoid this, try applying cream blush over the foundation. Cream blush has moisturizers in the formula to keep it soft and creamy. After applying, powder the face and then add powder blush. The powder blush will adhere better to the cheeks and not settle into the dry areas. Makeup professionals call this technique "piggy backing," as the powder blush "piggy backs" over the cream formula.

Healthy hues

While neutral is best for foundation, blush color is different. Often blush colors that are in the brown, beige, or sand color family look murky, and either do not add enough color or worse, add too much color and create a bruised effect on the face. Soft shades such as rose, muted plum, soft pink, peach, or even tawny colors in powder blush look much more natural on the face.

Forget frost and iridescent finishes on blush, they accentuate any lines on the face. Opt for one of the newer light-diffusing formulas. They will still add a little luminescence without settling or focusing on a facial line.

Do you know the time?

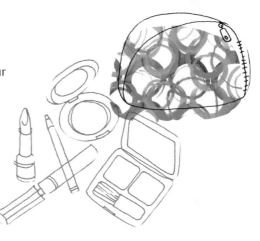

When is the last time you updated your look? The vital sign that it is time to rethink your makeup is when you can no longer find your favorite shade of product—it has been discontinued. Cosmetic companies never drop best sellers—the most popular shades—only the outdated ones.

Another sure way to know you need to change your ways is if you can virtually dress in the dark. You know the outfit, the makeup colors, and could dry your hair without looking. Finally, the dead look giveaway is when you see yourself in photographs and the only thing that changes is the season! Give it up, and get a new look!

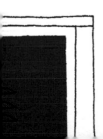

Chapter 3
Tool kit

Now you're cooking

You would not think of cooking a meal without the proper utensils, such as spoons, spatulas, or knives, so why would you attempt to apply your makeup du jour without the proper brushes? Good brushes, as in good cookware, are just as important to the beauty recipe as any ingredient that you use. A good set of brushes should last indefinitely. Invest in natural bristle brushes and make sure that the handle feels comfortable in your hand. Choose various sizes to meet your different makeup needs. Many companies offer complete sets, but the perfect combination for you might include a couple of brushes from several different companies.

It is important that you feel happy with your selection, as you are the one who will be using them day in and day out. Choose brushes that feel luxuriously soft against your skin, so you can take pleasure in making up your face.

Paint by numbers

If you are having trouble finding the perfect makeup brush at your beauty store, try an art supply store. Artists work with all kinds, shapes, sizes, and widths of brushes to achieve their desired artistic effects. Now you can too. If you find just the right size and thickness, but would prefer a bit more of an angled edge, do like the artists do and trim it to fit your needs.

Application 101

First and foremost, take all of the eye shadow applicators, blush brushes, powder puffs, and brushes that come with the products you purchase and toss them. Do not even attempt to use them. They do not do a good job. They are just there to fill space and make the product look easy to apply. Opt to use only professional brushes—toss away sponges and puffs you can't control. A professional application calls for professional tools. Don't keep the cheap!

Clear the way

Clear makeup bags are a great way to carry cosmetics in your handbag. You can see what you are searching for, and if you put a flat mirror right inside, next to the plastic, with the mirror facing you, you can repair smears or replenish lipstick in a jiffy.

Fishing for compliments

Rather than using an expensive train case to keep your makeup in one place, do as the pros do and keep makeup organized with a fishing tackle box. It comes with a carrying handle, and top and bottom compartments with lots of small storage trays which are perfect for keeping colors together. Plus, the case will hold bobby pins, head bands, tissues, cotton swabs, and balls—everything in one place, ready for anything. Plastic is the material of choice, since it is easy to wipe down if something spills and will not rust like metal. Plastic cases are also lighter to carry—even when loaded with all of your makeup stash.

Puff stuff

Powder puffs are definitely glamorous and it's fun to dab the face with a big fluffy puff, like in the movies. But be careful with puffs; they can harbor bacteria, excess skin oils, and stale makeup. If you simply must have a puff to put on your makeup, try a circular sponge to gently press in the powder. Be sure to toss when the sponge becomes soiled. Keep the big fluffy puff to apply powder to the décolleté and shoulders. Perfect for powders with tiny sparkles—now that is glamorous!

Make me blush

A blush brush should be of medium size and width, with a rounded top. The brush should feel soft and easy to manage as it glides over the skin. You must be able to deposit blush color precisely on the skin and softly blend and fade it out. Perfectly round rouge circles on the cheeks only work in cartoons.

Take a powder

Face powder brushes need to be big and fluffy. Extra big face powder brushes will glide the powder onto the skin without depositing too much product in one particular area, creating a soft veil. The brush bristles need to be soft to allow face powder to move with the facial contours and be flawlessly applied over the face. Plus a big powder brush makes us feel so feminine and downright sexy! Enjoy the experience of being a glamour gal.

Like a sponge

Foundation and concealer are best blended with a sponge. Triangular sponges adapt most easily to the facial contours, especially those areas around the nose and eyes. The sponge also allows you to blend foundation gently into the hairline and jawline, creating a flawless finish. As an added bonus, the sponge acts like a big eraser which can blend, smooth, or remove any makeup messes such as unblended powder, blush, or eye shadow.

Ring-a-ding

Our fourth finger, also called the ring finger, serves as a built-in makeup and skincare application tool. The ring finger is perfect as it exerts the least amount of pressure, so it is wonderful for working around the tender eye area with both color and treatment products. When you are working near the eyes, use your ring finger to gently apply the product without pulling on the skin. By patting with the finger as you apply product, you gently add warmth and increase product spreadability without stressing the skin.

In the shadows

Eye shadow brushes can be as varied as the eye shadow colors we wear.
A small brush with round bristles on the top can apply an overall color
across the eyelids without streaking. An angled brush can put color close
to the lash line, creating a liner look using eye shadow. A slightly tapered
end brush can contour the crease with ease. Whichever brush you choose,
be sure to blend your eye color!

Eyes wide open

A lash comb is a must-have in your makeup bag. Mascara can clump
at any moment during application. In addition, you can suffer from an
eyelash smudge if you have to rub your eyes. An eyelash comb rids
lashes of clumps—pronto. The comb is also great for separating
lashes and helping to define every lash.

Get to the point

When choosing a pencil sharpener for your eye, lip, and brow pencils, opt for ones that have at least two different size openings. Sharpeners that have a closed top cover to catch the shavings are also a good idea in order to keep cleaning to a minimum. The best sharpeners are found in the school supply department. Cosmetic companies often say when selling their pencils that only their sharpener will work. That is not true. A sharpener is a sharpener. Choose the one that gives you the most options. Perfect makeup applications require getting to the point!

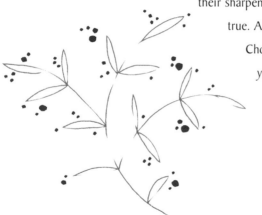

Curl up

One tool every beautiful eye has in common is an eyelash curler. The curler allows for a gentle upward turn to the lashes and gives the eyes a wide-open look. Always curl the lashes before applying mascara, since curling over mascara causes lashes to break off. To use, look straight into the mirror, place the lash curler as close to the upper lid as possible, squeeze the curler closed, count to 20 and release. Apply mascara as usual and see for yourself the glorious results!

Crimping your style

If your lashes absolutely, positively will not curl with an eyelash curler, beat them at their own game. Using a lash curler, begin at the base of the lashes and clamp on for a count of 20. Release curler and move halfway down the lash and repeat, closing and holding for a count of 20. Finally, open and clamp on the tips for the last count of 20. Even the most stubborn of stick-straight lashes will "bend" to this technique. If not, you may want to consider lash perming. The process lasts for about four to six weeks, which is about the life of a lash anyway.

Brow raising

Brow brushes are typically angled, with a stiffer texture. This allows a stronger concentration of color to be deposited on the brow. For best results, choose a brush that allows the skin under the brow to be colored. This will create the most believable brow color. A perfect addition to the angled brow brush is a toothbrush that is used to put brows in place after applying brow color.

Tweeze squeeze

A good pair of tweezers will last a lifetime. Invest in a quality, professional pair. Tweezers can be flat topped, pointed, or slanted. Tweezer shape is a personal choice that depends on your ability to manipulate the tweezers to remove only one hair at a time. Professionals suggest the slanted tip tweezer because it allows better control; with the tip side up, hairs can be removed with ease. If tips become dull, lightly rub a bit of sandpaper over the tip area once or twice. Rinse and dry.

Wipe out

If you have room, pack a travel container of baby wipes in your makeup bag. Perfect for removing smudges and getting hands clean after a touch up. Read the label and get the plainest ones that you can. Extra ingredients such as skin softeners or moisturizers could create a breakout. Keep it simple. You are just using them to clean up, not as a beauty treatment.

See the light

Proper makeup application calls for proper lighting. You don't get dressed in the dark, and you should not apply your face there either. Change the light bulbs in your grooming area to bulbs of at least 60 watts, or if using the makeup mirror type of bulb, check the wattage to make sure that the bulbs are at least 25 watts each.

Handle with care

All makeup accessories such as brushes, sponges (if not the toss-away kind), powder puffs, and tweezers need to be kept clean. At least once a month, wash items in an anti-bacterial soap and water solution. Rinse well, put brushes back in original shape, and allow them to air-dry. It is a good idea to mix $\frac{1}{4}$ cup of alcohol and $\frac{3}{4}$ cup of water in a spray mister and mist after each use to ward off bacteria. You wouldn't eat with unclean utensils—so don't use them on your face either!

Chapter 4

Read my lips

You wear it well

Purchasing a new lipstick color is almost as exciting as buying a new pair of shoes. Trying on either one is an immediate mood booster as both have instant eye appeal and feel rich and sexy against the skin.

Unlike any other cosmetic product, lipstick is the quickest way to make a statement about your personality—demure or determined, austere or outrageous, subtle or sexy, economy or first class. These statements are not created by product brand or price, but are generated by choices of color, texture, and intensity. Just as we have a closet full of different shoes to complement various outfits, so we need a makeup bag stocked with different lipsticks to match our mood. Pale and professional by day or vibrant and vampy by night—let lipstick transform your look instantly.

Keep it simple

There is no need for a fortress of lip liners. One or two liners
will do. Choose a staple color—neutral, bare, or mauve. The
purpose of a lip liner is to outline the lips to keep the lip color
from straying up and out of the lip area into any fine lines around
your lips. Another great use for lip liner is
to first fill in the lips with lip liner before
applying lip color. This keeps the lip
color from fading. You can own
a plethora of lipstick colors
but a neutral and/or
mauve-colored
lip liner is all
you really need
to give yourself
great lip service.

Lip luxury

A lip brush is a glamorous way to apply lip color. The best shape for a lip color brush is one that is tapered on both sides with a slightly rounded tip in the center. The bristles of the brush should be firm, but not so firm that applying lip color is not fluid.

Lip color should glide on effortlessly with a back and forth motion. Be sure to choose a lip brush that has a top that closes securely. You only want lip color on your mouth—not all over the inside of your purse!

Lip service

Putting lipstick on unconditioned lips is like applying paint over existing wallpaper. It just doesn't work. All you get is a look that is cakey, flaky, dull, and dry. Lips are meant to be enjoyed—both by an admirer and by you. Decide right here and now to exfoliate the lips once or twice a week with a lip exfoliator.

Apply the compound over the lips and allow it to dry. Gently rub the lips back and forth with a finger to remove the exfoliator—it's best to remove it over a sink, or with a washcloth underneath to catch the debris. After all of the gunk of leftover lipstick and dry skin flakes are removed, rinse the lips with a warm, wet washcloth. Pat dry and immediately slick on a lip conditioner. Lipstick will now go on shiny, sleek, moist, and rich!

Tone it down

If a lip color is a bit too bright after application, there are a couple of easy ways to tone it down. Try using a darker lip liner underneath the lipstick, as a base, to tone the color down, or you could try to put a dab of darker lip gloss on top of the intense lip color. Experiment by mixing colors right on the lips until you get the shade you absolutely love. The biggest trick of all is to remember how you got the color, so that you can recreate it later. The main thing is to have fun, experiment, and come up with your own signature color—or colors!

Miss congeniality

And the winner is—Miss Mauve Brown! A mauve/brown lip color
is a great neutral and universal color for the lips. It's a lip color
that works well on almost everyone so it is perfect as a handbag
or travel bag staple. If desperate, you can actually use it as a blush
by applying a little dab on the cheeks. It works equally as well
as a soft eye shadow in an emergency. Try patting a bit on
the eyelids as a quick pick-me-up for the face.
Be sure to pick a medium shade that is
neither too brown nor too mauve for
the most flattering results.

Lasting impression

Lipstick has the power to transform our faces. Even non-makeup wearers wear lip color. In fact, surveys show that, ten to one, lipstick is the number one product women will not be caught without! The average woman has at least five tubes of lipstick in her makeup bag at any given time. Lip color comes in tubes, pots, wands, squeeze tubes, pencils, and even roll-ons. There are thousands of colors with romantic names, all of which still captivate us. Lipstick can make us glamorous, sexy, powerful, innocent, mysterious, or sporty—depending on the shade. Be it matte, shiny, frosted, creamy, or glossy, nothing makes a statement like lipstick. It is the easiest product to apply. Simply open the tube, roll up, and glide color on the lips. For a more glamorous application, use a lip liner to apply more precisely.

Why not create a bit of mystery and intrigue by creating your very own lip color signature? You could choose to always wear the same color family on your lips—perhaps a sultry, sexy red suits your personality or maybe the playfulness of a jazzy shade of fuchsia is your calling card. When people see that color, they will think of you. Or you could totally keep them guessing by always wearing a lip color that exactly matches your clothing! Aaaah, the power of lipstick!

Thumbs up

The pad of the thumb is the
perfect place to test a lip color,
as the thumb's coloring is the
one part of the body that is
most similar to the natural color
of the lips. Most people tend to
rub the lip color on the back of the
hand to see if the color works with their

individual skin tone or not. The back of the hand serves the purpose
of comparing the lip color to your skin coloring, but it is the thumb
that will truly show you how the lip color will actually look on your lips.
Remember, never try out tester lip colors directly on your lips. Cosmetic
counter testers pick up all sorts of bacteria from other shoppers. You
want to leave the store with a brand new lipstick, not a nasty cold sore.

Shout pout

Make lips look their very poutiest—try putting a dot of cherry lip balm or a cherry color lip lacquer in the center of the lips and press together to distribute the color evenly between your top and bottom lips. The shiny balm or gloss will attract light to the mouth creating an illusion of plumper, fuller-looking lips. And since the color is a deep red, it will stain your mouth and last longer on the lips due to the cherry color's pigmentation. Give yourself a pout to shout about!

Flattery will get you everywhere

To find the most flattering lip color for you, match it up. The color just inside your mouth, closest to the lips, is a perfect color to match to, since that color is unique to you. Another good way to match it up is to purse your lips together for 30 seconds. The color that comes into the lips will be a natural hue for you. Nature produced it just for you—try it and see.

Downsize

If you feel that your lips are too big, downsize them by skipping the lip liner and choosing a neutral shade of color. Avoid glossy textures, as they add weight to the lips. Also, coloring just inside the natural lip line creates the illusion of a smaller-sized pout.

Line up

To avoid a harsh line when using lip liner, gently smudge the liner with a cotton swab after applying. If you find that the lip liner is still obvious, try putting on your lip color before lining. The lip color and liner will wear off together, avoiding leftover ring-around-the-mouth liner.

Silent partner

If you have been avoiding darker, richer lip colors because of feathering, outline the lips with a nude lip liner or one of the new invisible kinds that go on clear. This will create a barrier to help keep lipstick in its place and off the feather trail. These liners also work great with the super-shine kind of lip color that tends to run and smear.

A sunshine smile

Some lipsticks will make teeth look brighter than others. To get the brightest looking smile, choose colors that contrast with the teeth. Yellow-based colors, including corals and rich, warm brown shades, will make the teeth look more yellowish. Yellowish is not a good color for teeth—or for you! The best

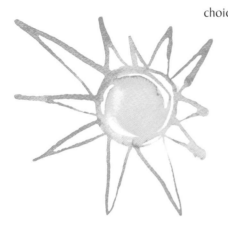

choices for brighter smiles are pinks, reds, and burgundies. If you love the look of coral or brown shades, choose one that has a more pinkish tone rather than a yellow tint, in order to show off your brightest smile.

Tape measure

If your lipstick begins to cake up or flake while wearing, a quick way to remove the cakes and flakes is to lick your lips, then press on a piece of cellophane tape. Gently peel off, simultaneously removing the tape and all the gunk from the surface of your lips. To avoid over-pulling the lip skin, be sure that your lips are wet before putting the tape on. Slick on a bit of lip conditioner and reapply lipstick on top.

Take it to the max

To create the fullest lips possible, stay away from very deep lip colors. Deep shades, especially matte textures, make the lips look small and taut. Use a lip liner that is very close to your own natural lip color and add a bit of shine. Textures that catch the light create an illusion of bigger, fuller lips. Be sure not to go too light in color choices either, as you want the lips to be noticed—not neutral.

On the run

The more guidable and spreadable the lip color is, the more likely it is to run or bleed over the lip line, soaking into any vertical lines, and onto the skin. Glosses, wet-shine lip lacquers, and lip colors in pots or wands tend to run the most after application. You want the color to spread and be easy to apply so you don't pull on the lip area, but it should have some "oomph" to it once it has been applied. If lip color has a nasty habit of smearing onto your teeth, here's a quick trick. After lip gloss application, pop a finger between your pouting lips and pull it out slowly. Any excess color will come off on your finger! Lipstick should not slide across the finish line—in the case of lip color, running is not winning!

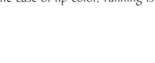

All puckered up

Puckered lips can create an uneven surface that lipstick often "skips," resulting in an uneven application. If this happens to you, stretch out your lips between your second and third finger when applying lip color to get the entire lip filled in. You will have a smooth application and will find that your lipstick lasts longer too.

To avoid over-emphasizing the puckered look, choose shiny lipsticks and lip glosses that glide over any lines to give the illusion of smoother lips. Matte lipsticks will only settle in the cracks and accentuate a puckered pout—get that gloss on instead!

Smudge control

If your lipstick bleeds and runs no matter what, try
this model's trick. To keep lipstick in place under
the hot lights of the runway, models apply
concealer around all of the lip area.
The concealer keeps the lip color in
its place—on the lips and off the
face. Apply a small amount of
concealer all around the lip area,
patting in with your ring finger. Blend
with a sponge right up to the lip line
and then powder the area. Apply a lip
control cream to further prevent lipstick smears,
then apply lip color lightly. Blot the lips and kiss the
smudges goodbye!

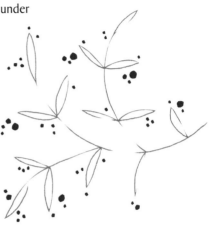

Sexy red

Nothing says sexy better than a red mouth. If you never felt that you could wear red, maybe you did not know which red to wear.

* Bright clear reds can be worn by all skin tones. The depth of the color is a personal choice.

* Blue reds are best on brunettes.

* Brown reds are a knockout on redheads.

* Tomato reds are best for fair skin and those with lighter eye colors.

When trying red for the first time, apply it and view it in different lights such as natural, office, and home light. At first it may look too bright, but keep checking it in the mirror—without a doubt, this sexy shade will begin to grow on you.

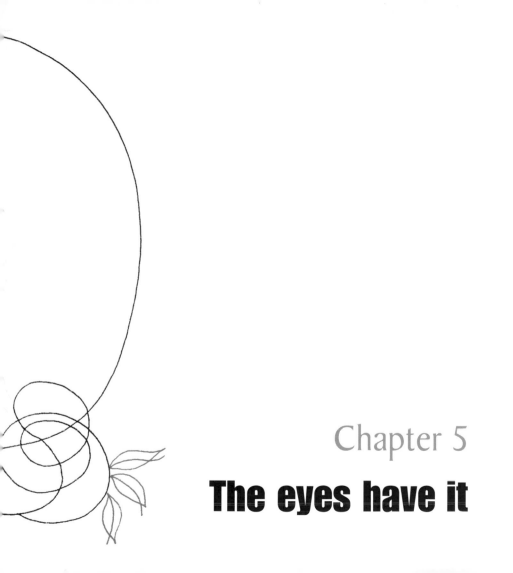

Chapter 5

The eyes have it

Eye-opening options

Eye shadow comes in several different forms, from powder or cream, to pencils or pots. All the colors look beautiful in the containers, but how they look on the eyes is what counts. Creams, pencils, and pot colors tend to be much more difficult and messy to apply and, more importantly, are less likely to have the staying power of powder.

Eye shadow powder is the best choice for day in, day out, tried and true wear. Powders are so versatile—you can use a wet powder shadow for more definition, to line the eyes, or as a soft overall color for the entire eyelid. Some powders can be drying and settle in the eye creases, so to make sure that the shadow goes on smooth, test the color by rubbing a bit on the back of the hand. If it is finely textured, glides well, and looks fresh without being too dry or too moist, it will most likely be perfect.

Eye know

Eye shadow is meant to flatter the shape and color of our eyes. A lighter, neutral color is usually the best choice to apply to the entire eyelid as a color base. Neutrals encompassing beige, vanilla, mauve, cream, and even subtle gold tones serve as great base shadow colors on the eyes. Begin by sweeping the eye shadow brush along the lash line and moving upward to the area under the brow. Sweep the brush back and forth until all color is blended.

To create a subtle, smoky depth to the eyes, add a bit of contour color. Depending on what color you have chosen as your overall eye shadow color, complement the color family with a contour shade. Contour colors include charcoal gray, milky brown, deeper plum, taupe, and even navy. Using a smaller eye shadow brush, begin at the lash line of the outermost corner of the eyelid, add the contour color, brushing the color inward covering about $^1/_3$ of the eyelid. If your eyes are on the smaller side, go inwards only $^1/_4$ of the way. Carry the contour color all along the orbital bone (the bone in which your eye sits). This creates depth to the eye socket. Gently blend color until no start or stop color lines are apparent.

In the spotlight

Highlighting is a great way to add a little bit of pizzazz to the eye area, right under your brow bone, and in the center of the eyelid. Take a little bit of accent color such as matte gold, delicate, demure pink, or slightly iridescent beige, and add a bit right under the arch of the brow. Also add a bit to the center of the eyelid under any contouring color. This technique is called spot lighting. It is subtle enough not to be obvious, but outstanding enough to be noticed.

Drop the droop

To give lift to a droopy top eyelid, sweep light-colored eye shadow all over your eyelid. Then apply a little of the same eye shadow with a cotton swab underneath your eyes, sweeping it slightly upward from the bottom of the lashes moving up toward the outer corner of the eye. Use a slightly darker contour eye shadow color only on the outermost corners of the eyes to create a smoky, rich look, without adding too much depth to the area. Apply an extra coat of mascara on the lashes just above the iris of the eye to draw attention to the center of your eyes rather than the troublesome corners.

Bat an eye

Black mascara is like the little black dress. It's perfect for any and all occasions. Black mascara adds definition to the eyes and allows the lashes to frame the eyes, showcasing eye color. The only time the use of brown mascara is warranted is if you are a member of the redhead family. Auburn and strawberry blondes can be overpowered by black, so they should stick to dark brown. Other than these two, there are no exceptions to black lashes!

Brow beat

If "unruly" is a perfect description of your brow hair, try a brow setting product. Brow set comes in a mascara tube, complete with a mascara-type wand. The difference is that the contents are clear or creamy and turn clear when set. To apply, color your brows as usual. Comb them gently into place and brush your brows with the brow set, following the shape you have created. Once it dries, "wild hairs" will be a thing of past. Think of brow set as mousse for your brows.

Seeing red

Stay away from eyebrow pencils with even a hint of red—this tip goes for redheads too! The "ginger" brow look is very fake looking. Sometimes redheads feel that they should use a red-based eyebrow pencil—but this is not the case. Red-based pencils, as mild as they appear, always turn out way too red to be real. Choose instead a brow coloring that has a hint of light brown, maybe mixed with blonde, or light taupe, for the most natural—and believable—brow. As a rule, lips and eyes should look "done," but skin and brows should look natural.

Bottom line it

Eyes will stand out even better if you line the bottom lash line with a lighter eyeliner color than you use on the top. For example, dramatize the eyes by applying brown underneath the bottom lashes and black kohl to the top. The contrast creates interest without being overly dramatic. For lighter eye color and/or a softer effect, line the underneath bottom lashes with taupe eyeliner and apply charcoal gray on the top. Test out different color combinations to see what works best for your eye shape and color.

Perfect Makeup

Line them up

Eyeliner can make the eyes look beautiful and glamorous. Although colors are as vast as the rainbow, opt for those that are subtle and coordinate with your eye shadow. Eyeliner comes in liquid, pencil, powder, and gel. All of the choices have merit, depending on the look you want. But hands down, pencil and powder liners are easier to maneuver. After the base color of eye shadow is applied, hold the lid a tiny bit taut, without stretching the skin, and apply liner on top of the lid next to the lashes. For best results apply color gently in back and forth brush-like strokes. The effect will be a smoky eye, not a drawn on line. On the bottom, line with the same brush strokes as close to the bottom lashes as possible. After applying, take your eye shadow brush and pat the basic all-over eye shadow color that you have chosen to wear onto the liner to set the liner for all-day wear.

Pass on the proof

Waterproof mascara is not good for the lashes—period. It is very drying and has the tendency to increase lash breakage. Waterproof formulas contain ingredients geared to coat the lash and prevent water from entering. As a result, when the mascara has dried after application, it shrinks the lashes, causing them to fall out. Plus, if watery eyes or crying are the reasons why you are wearing it, it will not work anyway, since we rub our eyes when we cry. Rubbing destroys the mascara, even if it is waterproof. It is not worth losing lashes over—opt for the regular mascara.

Be still

In this hurry up, go, go, go world, some things should not be rushed. Putting on mascara is one of them. Be still and complete the process. Moving while putting on mascara is dangerous for your eyes. Since we tend to brush on mascara at warp speed anyway, doing so while on the train, bus, or subway, or while walking, only increases the chances of putting the brush in your eye. A scratched cornea is not beautiful on anyone!

Tint hint

Eyelash and eyebrow tinting is a great way to wear color. Tinting, using a vegetable dye and done professionally in a spa, allows lashes and brows to have color for about four weeks. This method is great for fair-haired gals whose natural coloring tends to be neutral. Plus, having your brows and lashes already done helps speed up the already-rushed morning makeup application.

Short-term

Mascara is definitely the shortest of our short-term products. Three to four months is the maximum life span for mascara once it has been opened. Since mascara comes into contact with our eyelashes, which are the closest thing to the bodily fluids in the eye, contaminants are pretty much a given.

When used daily, three months is about the tube's capacity, but either way, after four months, it needs to be tossed. And it should go without saying—never, never, never, use anyone else's mascara— not even once. An eye infection is not only not pretty, but is also pretty scary to say the least!

Falsies

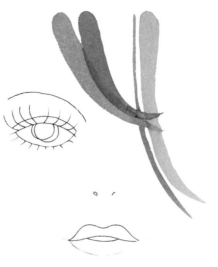

False eyelashes are great for special occasions, although they can be tricky to apply. While the lash strip makes the false lashes easier to apply, it can look obvious unless applied perfectly. To apply, put a thin line of eyelash adhesive on the strip and look directly into a mirror. Using the hand like an airplane that is landing, sweep down over the top of your real lashes, center the false ones and press down in the middle and on both ends to seal. If this is too hard to master, it may be better to use individual lashes on the outer corners of your eyes. Dot the roots of the individual lashes with a bit of glue, then guide them into place using a pair of tweezers. You may want a professional to show you how to apply both the individual and the strip kind. Once you learn, it is like driving—you will always know how.

Luscious lashes

To make lashes their most luscious, add a lash thickener to your makeup routine. A lash thickener is a lash conditioning product containing elements that help keep lashes hydrated and silky looking, as well as thicker and richer looking when mascara is applied. Some formulas are actually colored like mascara, so you can add a bit of color while you condition. It is also a good nighttime treatment; simply coat the clean lashes before going to bed. This is a perfect treatment for dry and brittle lashes or brows.

Spit it out!

Do not under any circumstances wet caked mascara with saliva. Our saliva contains all kinds of bacteria. Only use pure, filtered water or oil-free toner to wet the cake to get the mascara moist.

Pump not

Contrary to popular belief, pumping mascara is not a good idea. Pumping the mascara wand into the mascara container does nothing except allow air into the container and cause the mascara to dry out more quickly.

To revive dry mascara for a few more applications, run the closed container under warm water for about one minute before applying. This method will extend the tube for about four or five more uses. After that, toss it out and open a new one.

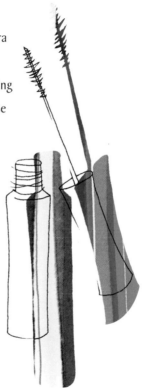

Open up

To best open up the eyes with mascara, start with the bottom lashes by applying a light coating of mascara. On the top lashes, using the mascara wand, gently zigzag the applicator back and forth. (The zigzag technique will not only color the lashes but also help to separate each lash and reduce the risk of clumping.) Then place the mascara wand on top of the lashes and roll out from the base of the lash all the way to the lash tip. This will coat the top of the lashes and create a thicker coat and fuller look. Take a moment to zigzag back up after rolling the top lashes, since the rolling technique, while excellent for coating lashes, has a tendency to make them droop.

Apply a second coat if needed, but since this technique adds both color and length to the lashes, you may only need one.

Eye care

If mascara makes your eyes water, or if you have sensitive eyes, choose a brand that is designed specifically for sensitive eyes. In some cases, wax can be an irritant, and sensitive formulas contain less wax then regular kinds. The sensitive mascara has more silk protein powders added to it to help 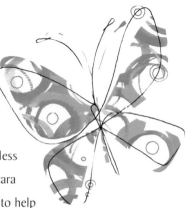 coat the lashes without using wax. A lot of cosmetic companies have added a range of mascara for sensitive eyes and/or contact lens wearers. Check out the different brands, and see which one works best for you.

Most important of all, a tip that is worth repeating—never, ever use anyone else's mascara! Keep it personal!

Evening eyes

If your evening-out plans include dancing, keep eye shadow from smearing and fading by using this little trick. Wet the shadow before applying, but instead of using water, which can crack after a while, moisten the shadow with a drop or two of eyedrops designed to get the red out. The eyedrops will form a paste with the shadow and allow for a smoother application. Allow to dry and you are all set to dance the night away!

Cream the cream

Cream eye shadows, while tempting in color selections, will never look natural as they are so difficult to apply. Creams tend to crease, smear, and are virtually impossible to blend properly with other shades. If you are going to experiment with them, try using your finger to apply the cream to the eyelid, as this will warm the product slightly and make it spread more easily. However, for the most long lasting color-look, stick to powder.

Susie Galvez

Armed with quick wit, years of professional experience, and more get-pretty tips than a beauty pageant coordinator, expert makeup artist, esthetician, and author Susie Galvez is dedicated to giving women the tools to help them accept themselves and realize that each day is another chance to be beautiful. Inspired by the thrill she gets from helping women rediscover beauty on a daily basis, Susie wrote the *Ooh La La! Effortless Beauty* series which includes *Ooh La La! Perfect Face, Ooh La La! Perfect Body, Ooh La La! Perfect Makeup*, and *Ooh La La! Perfect Hair*.

Susie is also the author of *Hello Beautiful: 365 Ways to Be Even More Beautiful, Weight Loss Wisdom: 365 Successful Dieting Tips*, and *InSPArations: Ideas, tips & techniques to increase employee loyalty, client satisfaction, and bottom line spa profits*.

In addition to writing, Susie owns Face Works Day Spa in Richmond, Virginia. Face Works Day Spa has been featured in national and consumer magazines such as *Allure, Cosmopolitan, Elle*, and *Town and Country*, as well as many trade publications, including *Skin, Inc., Dermascope, Day Spa*,

Salon Today, *Nails Plus*, *Nails*, *Spa Management*, and *Les Nouvelles Esthetiques*. In April 2002, The Day Spa Association recognized Face Works as one of only 12 fully accredited day spas—out of 1,000 members—in the United States.

Susie is also recognized as one of the leading consultants in the spa industry, and is in high demand as a speaker at international spa conventions. She is a featured spokesperson for the beauty industry on radio and television programs, and is a member of Cosmetic Executive Women, The National Association of Women Business Owners, and the Society of American Cosmetic Chemists.

You can contact Susie at www.susiegalvez.com or by visiting her beauty website at www.beautyatyourfingertips.com where you will find even more ways to have Ooh La La moments! Be sure to sign up for your free spa-at-home tips!

Special appreciation

"Follow your bliss." Joseph Campbell

This book could not have been completed without the unwavering support and love from my very special friends. Thank you for allowing me to follow my bliss:

Judith Ann Graham, thank you for sharing the excitement of the latest color, texture, or technique with me.

Sandy Clemons, who was a friend at first sight. Thanks for your encouragement.

Thank you Aunt Esther for teaching me what two beauty essentials never to be without—lipstick and a mirror.

Audra Baca, whose youthful spirit and turn of the word captured "me" on paper.

Dottie Dehart and Celia Rocks for their persistence in carrying my message out to the multitudes day after day.

Zaro Weil, friend and publisher, who entrusted me with her title.

To the superb staff at Face Works Day Spa who are responsible for creating perfect Ooh La La moments for all of our clients.

And lastly, but always first with me, thank you Tino Galvez, who is truly the wind beneath my wings.

XOXO

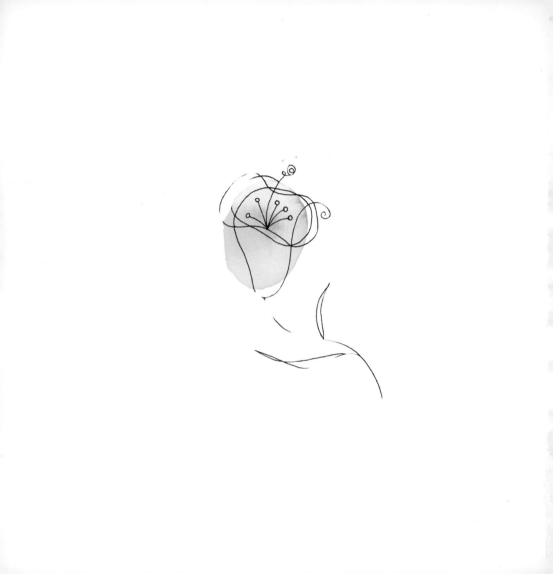